GAULISH VILLAGE

COMPENDIUM

LAUDANUM

AQUARIUM

TOTORUM

A R M O R I C A

LUTETIA

SPQR

B E L G I C A

GAUL
(ROMAN CONQUEST)
50 B.C.

C E L T I C A

P R O V I N C I A

A Q U I T A N I A

The year is 50 BC. Gaul is entirely occupied by the Romans.
Well, not entirely... One small village of indomitable Gauls still
holds out against the invaders. And life is not easy for the
Roman legionaries who garrison the fortified camps of
Totorum, Aquarium, Laudanum and Compendium...

a few of the Gauls

Asterix, the hero of these adventures. A shrewd, cunning little warrior; all perilous missions are immediately entrusted to him. Asterix gets his superhuman strength from the magic potion brewed by the druid Getafix…

Obelix, Asterix's inseparable friend. A menhir delivery-man by trade; addicted to wild boar. Obelix is always ready to drop everything and go off on a new adventure with Asterix – so long as there's wild boar to eat, and plenty of fighting.

Getafix, the venerable village druid. Gathers mistletoe and brews magic potions. His speciality is the potion which gives the drinker superhuman strength. But Getafix also has other recipes up his sleeve…

Cacofonix, the bard. Opinion is divided as to his musical gifts. Cacofonix thinks he's a genius. Everyone else thinks he's unspeakable. But so long as he doesn't speak, let alone sing, everybody likes him…

Finally, Vitalstatistix, the chief of the tribe. Majestic, brave and hot-tempered the old warrior is respected by his men and feared by his enemies. Vitalstatistix himself has only one fear; he is afraid the sky may fall on his head tomorrow. But as he always says, 'Tomorrow never comes.'

ASTERIX AND THE NORMANS

TEXT BY GOSCINNY

DRAWINGS BY UDERZO

TRANSLATED BY ANTHEA BELL AND DEREK HOCKRIDGE

HODDER DARGAUD
LONDON SYDNEY AUCKLAND

Asterix and the Normans

ISBN 0 340 22287 5 (cased edition)
ISBN 0 340 24307 4 (paperbound edition)

Copyright © 1966 Dargaud Editeur
English language text copyright © 1978 Hodder & Stoughton Ltd

First published in Great Britain 1978 (cased)
Second impression 1978

First published in Great Britain 1979 (paperbound)
Sixth impression 1984

Printed in Belgium for Hodder Dargaud Ltd,
Mill Road, Dunton Green, Sevenoaks, Kent TN13 2YJ
by Henri Proost & Cie, Turnhout

ANOTHER PEACEFUL DAY HAS DAWNED IN THE LITTLE VILLAGE WE KNOW SO WELL...

LOOK, DARLING! THE ARMS AND ARMOUR FIRM HAS SENT ITS MAIL ORDER CATALOGUE AT LAST!

WHY, THERE'S POSTALDISTRIX THE POSTMAN!

NOTHING FOR US, POSTALDISTRIX?

NO. I HAVE A LETTER FOR CHIEF VITALSTATISTIX TO DELIVER, AND THAT'S ALL!

WE'LL GO WITH YOU.

CAN YOU SEND MENHIRS BY POST?

YES, BUT IT'S A GOOD IDEA TO REGISTER THEM IN CASE THEY GET LOST.

A LETTER FROM LUTETIA, O CHIEF VITALSTATISTIX!

OH, THAT MUST BE FROM MY BROTHER DOUBLEHELIX ...THOUGH HE DOESN'T ENGRAVE VERY OFTEN!

OH!

NOTHING GRAVE ENGRAVED THERE, I HOPE?

NO, MY BROTHER DOUBLEHELIX HAS A SON CALLED JUSTFORKIX, AND IT SEEMS MY NEPHEW IS GETTING A BIT SOFT LIVING IN LUTETIA. DOUBLEHELIX IS SENDING HIM HERE FOR A HOLIDAY. HE WANTS US TO MAKE A MAN OF HIM!

I HOPE I CAN COUNT ON YOU, FRIENDS?

BY THE TIME WE'RE THROUGH WITH HIM HE'LL BE HUNTING BOAR WITH HIS BARE HANDS!

YOU MEAN THERE'S SOME OTHER WAY TO DO IT?

5

WATCH OUT!

BY TOUTATIS!

HE'S CRAZY!

CLUCK CLUCK
YELP YELP YELP

I SHALL THROW THE ARMS AND ARMOUR FIRM'S MAIL ORDER CATALOGUE AT HIM IF HE DOESN'T LOOK OUT!

SCREEECH!

YELP YELP YELP

HI, UNCLE! I'M YOUR NEPHEW JUSTFORKIX!

?!

ER... VERY NICE TO SEE YOU, JUSTFORKIX... LET ME INTRODUCE ASTERIX AND OBELIX...

I'VE NEVER SEEN A CHARIOT LIKE THAT BEFORE...

NO, YOU WOULDN'T GET MANY OF THESE AROUND HERE... IT'S A SPORTS CHARIOT MADE IN MEDIOLANUM*...

*MILAN

RIGHT, LET'S START.

START WHAT?

START MAKING A MAN OF HIM, OF COURSE! THE WAY TO START MAKING A MAN OF HIM IS TO START THUMPING HIM!

NO, NO, THAT'S NOT THE WAY.

OH, AND JUST HOW DOES MISTER ASTERIX THINK WE'RE GOING TO START MAKING A MAN OF HIM IF WE DON'T START THUMPING HIM SO AS TO START MAKING A MAN OF HIM?

WE WANT HIM TO TRUST US!

WE'RE GOING TO HOLD A BALL IN YOUR HONOUR, JUSTFORKIX!

YOU PEASANTS DANCE OUT HERE IN THE STYX?*

* GLOOMY CLASSICAL ALLUSION

HOW QUAINT!

YOU KNOW, OBELIX, I'M NOT SURE YOU WEREN'T RIGHT ABOUT THUMPING HIM!

SEE?

WOOF!

WHILE ALL THIS IS GOING ON IN GAUL, LET US TRAVEL FAR AWAY, TO THE NORTHERN LANDS WHERE WINTERS ARE HARD AND THE NIGHT LASTS FOR MONTHS ON END... LANDS INHABITED BY **THE NORSEMEN,** OR NORMANS, AS THE PEOPLE OF GAUL KNEW THEM. THEY ARE GREAT CONQUERORS...

WE GIVE THE GAULS A MISS FOR ONCE AND THAT LOT MAKE A NORMAN CONQUEST OF US!

THEY WORSHIP THOR, THE GOD OF WAR, AND ODIN, WHO INVITES WARRIORS SLAIN IN BATTLE TO FEAST WITH HIM IN VALHALLA...

WON'T!

AND THEY DO NOT KNOW THE MEANING OF FEAR!

IF YOU DON'T FINISH YOUR NICE CREAM SOUP THE TROLL WILL COME AND EAT YOU UP!

BY THOR, THAT'S A LAUGH!

THIS IS A NUISANCE, SINCE NOT ONLY ARE THE CHILDREN NOT SCARED OF TROLLS, BUT AS FEAR OF THE AUTHORITIES ENCOURAGES PRUDENCE, NORSE ROADS ARE FAR FROM SAFE...

WHAT DO YOU MEAN BY IT, TRYING TO PASS A FOUR-REINDEER-POWER POLICE CHARIOT AT THE TOP OF A HILL???

SO WHAT? MINE'S A NORSE-DRAWN CHARIOT!

...AND IT IS PRACTICALLY IMPOSSIBLE TO CURE HICCUPS...

HAVE YOU OR HAVE YOU NOT FINISHED HICCUPPING?

HIC! NO. HIC! WHY DO YOU ASK?

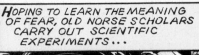

HOPING TO LEARN THE MEANING OF FEAR, OLD NORSE SCHOLARS CARRY OUT SCIENTIFIC EXPERIMENTS...

FEEL ANYTHING?

NO FEAR SO FAR, ONLY PAIN. HAVE ANOTHER GO.

SO CHIEF OLAF TIMANDAHAF ASSEMBLES HIS MEN...

WE CAN'T GO ON LIKE THIS! EVEN THE WEAKEST OF NATIONS KNOW ABOUT FEAR AND BEING FRIGHTENED... BUT NOT US!

AND WE PRIDE OURSELVES ON KNOWING EVERYTHING! EVERYTHING!

THUMP! THUMP! THUMP!

BUT LISTEN, O TIMANDAHAF, WHAT USE IS THIS THING FEAR THAT WE DON'T UNDERSTAND?

I'VE HEARD THAT FEAR LENDS YOU WINGS, BY ODIN. ONCE WE CAN FLY LIKE BIRDS WE'LL STICK AT NOTHING.

BY THOR!

BY ODIN!

BY GUM...

9

I SUGGEST WE START OUT TODAY FOR THE LANDS WHERE PEOPLE KNOW THE MEANING OF FEAR! WE'LL DEAL DEATH AND DESTRUCTION IF NECESSARY, BUT WE MUST AND WILL LEARN THE SECRET!

HEAR! HEAR!

WE'RE WITH YOU!

LONG LIVE CHIEF TIMANDAHAF!

AND I PROMISE YOU, WE SHALL COME HOME TO TELL AN ADMIRING WORLD: THE NORMANS KNOW THE MEANING OF FEAR! THE NORMANS ARE MORE FRIGHTENED THAN YOU!

NOW FOR OUR NATIONAL BEVERAGE, APPLE BRANDY DRUNK FROM THE SKULLS OF OUR ENEMIES! IT'S A VERY HEADY LIQUOR.

*SO THAT SAME NIGHT, I.E. THREE WEEKS LATER, A MIGHTY NORMAN LONGSHIP FULL OF FIERCE WARRIORS SETS OFF ON ITS UNUSUAL VOYAGE OF SCIENTIFIC DISCOVERY...

WHAT SHORE ARE WE MAKING FOR, O TIMANDAHAF?

I CHOSE ONE AT RANDOM, O NESCAF. WE'RE MAKING FOR GAUL.

WHICH SHOULD TEACH US ALL TO DISTRUST RANDOM SAMPLES, SINCE — AS WE KNOW THE GAULS ARE NOT TOO KNOWLEDGEABLE ABOUT THE MEANING OF FEAR EITHER. IN FACT, THEY FEAR ONLY ONE THING, THE SKY FALLING ON THEIR HEADS, AND THEY DON'T LET THAT KEEP THEM AWAKE AT NIGHT...

GET UP, LAZY! THE ROOSTER HAS CROWED TO LET US KNOW IT'S DAY!

RIGHT, THEN YOU DON'T NEED ME ANY MORE...

THIS IS THE TIME I GO TO BED IN LUTETIA.

OBELIX, HOW ABOUT HELPING HIM GET UP?

CAN I, ASTERIX? CAN I?

OUOUAAAAH!

PLAF!

HE SEEMS TO HAVE GOT OUT OF BED THE WRONG SIDE.

6 IX

10

11

THE NOR... THE NOR... THE NORM...

SEE, THAT'S LUTETIANS FOR YOU! THEY'RE ALWAYS IN A HURRY IN LUTETIA... JUST CAN'T TAKE LIFE AS IT COMES!

LUTETIA'S ALL RIGHT FOR A VISIT, BUT I DON'T FANCY LIVING THERE.

OH, I WAS LOOKING FOR YOU. I'VE BEEN THINKING ABOUT THE HIT I MIGHT MAKE IN LUTE...

CLUCK!

CLU... EEEK!

WHAT'S THE MATTER WITH HIM?

IT SEEMS THE NORMANS WANT TO INVADE US.

WE'RE OFF TO SEE THE CHIEF ABOUT IT. JUSTFORKIX WILL BE THERE BY NOW.

GOOD. I WANT TO ASK HIM ABOUT THE PALACE OF VARIETIX.

SOON AFTERWARDS.

YOU TWO GO AND SEE WHAT THE NORMANS ARE DOING. IF THEY'RE LANDING, WE THROW THEM BACK INTO THE SEA.

DO YOU THINK THEY'LL LAND, ASTERIX? HEY, DO YOU REALLY THINK SO?

I'LL GO AND MAKE A LITTLE MAGIC POTION, JUST IN CASE...

PSST... I WANT A WORD WITH YOU...

WELL, NORMANS APART, DO YOU LIKE IT HERE? NOT FEELING HOMESICK?

LIS...LISTEN, DO YOU KNOW WHO THE NORMANS ARE?

OF COURSE! THEY'RE FIERCE FIGHTERS, AND LIKE US THEY DON'T KNOW THE MEANING OF FEAR!

WE MAY LIVE IN THE PROVINCES, MY BOY, BUT THAT DOESN'T MEAN WE'RE OUT OF TOUCH!

CRAZY! THEY'RE ALL CRAZY!

RIGHT, CAN WE HAVE A TALK ABOUT MY FUTURE NOW?

TIMANDAHAF IS JUST FINISHING HIS VEAL IN CREAM SAUCE...

OH, SO YOU'RE BACK, NESCAF. WHAT NEWS?

I'VE BEEN LISTENING TO SOME OF THE GAULS. THEY DON'T KNOW THE MEANING OF FEAR EITHER.

WHAT? YOU MEAN WE'VE COME ALL THIS WAY FOR NO GOOD REASON?

CRACK!

I'VE A GOOD MIND TO PUT US ALL TO THE SWORD... MAYBE WE'LL LEARN THE REASON* FOR FEAR AT ODIN'S FEAST,* SINCE THESE GAULS ARE SO IGNORANT!

THEY DO AS GOOD A SOLE* AS WE COULD GET FROM OUR OWN ICE FLOES* THOUGH...

*SENTIMENTS ECHOED CENTURIES LATER BY ALEXANDER POPE...'THE FEAST OF REASON AND THE FLOW OF SOUL...'

ANYWAY, DON'T BOOK OUR TABLE YET! I DID HEAR ONE GAUL BOAST HE WAS AN EXPERT ON FEAR...

A REAL PROFESSIONAL, BY THOR! THAT'S WHAT WE NEED!

THE ONLY THING IS, WHEN HE'S WITH THE OTHER GAULS HE ISN'T SO FRIGHTENED...

GET AN EXPEDITIONARY FORCE TOGETHER! WE MUST CAPTURE HIM AND SHIELD HIM FROM THE DEBILITATING INFLUENCE OF HIS FRIENDS!

FEAR WILL LEND US WINGS, AND WE'LL SOON BE AIRBORNE... HAVE A LITTLE SKULL NESCAF?

I WON'T SAY NO... LET'S PUT OUR HEADS TOGETHER.

MEANWHILE, IN THE GAULISH VILLAGE...

I... I'VE DECIDED TO CUT MY HOLIDAY SHORT AND GO BACK TO LUTETIA...

WHAT, JUST WHEN THE REAL FUN'S STARTING? OH, DON'T GO, JUSTFORKIX! YOU'LL LEARN HOW TO FIGHT! WE GAULS NEVER GIVE QUARTER!

I PROMISE YOU THERE WON'T BE ANY GAULISH QUARTER!

I KNOW, BUT THERE'S A LATIN QUARTER AND I'D LIKE TO GET BACK TO IT!

13

YOU'RE QUITE SURE, JUSTFORKIX? MUST YOU REALLY GO?

WAIT A MINUTE, JUSTFORKIX! I'VE GOT A LITTLE PRESENT FOR YOU!

A PRESENT FROM ARMORICA

WELL, IT'S A PITY... YOUR FATHER WANTED ME TO TOUGHEN YOU UP A BIT... RUB THE CORNERS OFF YOU...

I WISH I COULD GO TO LUTETIA TOO...

CORNERS... CORNERS... HUH! I CAN CUT A FEW CORNERS MYSELF!

A PRES FROM

CRAAACK!

?

BOTHER THAT MENHIR! IT'S GONE AND BROKEN THE AXLE... I'M IN A TIGHT CORNER NOW! THE TROUBLE WITH THESE FOREIGN CHARIOTS IS GETTING SPARE PARTS...

A PRES FROM

AND CLOSE AT HAND.

WHAT A BIT OF LUCK! IT'S THE MAN WHO KNOWS THE MEANING OF FEAR! WE MUST GRAB HIM BEFORE HE FLIES AWAY!

NOW REMEMBER, EVERYONE, THE CHIEF SAID TO BRING HIM BACK ALIVE!

ALL THESE LITTLE SUBTLETIES!

19

IT'S A PITY JUSTFORKIX HAS LEFT... HE WAS SO FUNNY!

WELL, HE WOULDN'T STAY, SO ON HIS OWN HEAD BE IT... LET'S GO AND HUNT SOME BOAR IN THE FOREST. THAT'LL CHEER YOU UP.

I DO LIKE IT IN THE FOREST... WE MIGHT FIND BOARS, ROMANS, MUSHROOMS, MAYBE EVEN NORMANS...

I TELL YOU WHAT, IF WE FIND ANY BOARS, ROMANS OR NORMANS WE KNOCK THEM ON THE HEAD, IF WE FIND ANY MUSHROOMS WE ...

LOOK, DOGMATIX HAS STOPPED! HE'S PICKED UP A SCENT!

SNIFF SNIFF

LET'S FOLLOW HIM!

RIGHT. IF IT'S A BOAR WE'LL SHARE IT, IF IT'S A ROMAN OR A NORMAN YOU CAN LEAVE IT TO ME, IF IT'S A MUSHROOM I'LL LEAVE IT TO...

OH!

JUSTFORKIX'S CHARIOT!

A PRESENT FROM...

ISN'T DOGMATIX MARVELLOUS? I TAUGHT HIM TO PICK UP THE SCENT OF A MENHIR, SO HE'D MADE A GOOD HOUND...

SNIFF SNIFF

I THOUGHT I'D START WITH MENHIRS BECAUSE THEY DON'T MOVE AS FAST AS RABBITS...

THE AXLE'S BROKEN...

FLIMSY, I CALL IT. IT MAY BE FAST, BUT IT'S FLIMSY. PUT ONE TINY LITTLE MENHIR IN IT, AND SOMETHING BREAKS!

I CAN'T SEE JUSTFORKIX GOING OFF INTO THE FOREST ALONE...

NO, HE'D HAVE TAKEN THE MENHIR WITH HIM!

FOOT PRINTS... I'M AFRAID THE NORMANS MAY HAVE KIDNAPPED JUSTFORKIX!

LET'S TELL CHIEF VITALSTATISTIX!

YOU MEAN THEY WANTED A SOUVENIR, THEY FOUND JUSTFORKIX AND MY MENHIR AND THEY TOOK JUSTFORKIX? THESE NORMANS ARE CRAZY!

16 II

IN THE NORMAN CAMP, WHERE TIMANDAHAF IS JUST FINISHING A CHICKEN IN CREAM SAUCE...

WE GOT HIM, O TIMANDAHAF!

BY ODIN! LET'S GO AND SEE HIM RIGHT AWAY, O NESCAF!

HE DOESN'T LOOK TOO GOOD, NESCAF!

WE CLUBBED HIM TO STOP HIM FLYING AWAY, THE WAY WE CLUB BIRDS... NOT VERY TOUGH, THIS GAULISH RIFFRAFF!

COMING!

NO, NO ONE WANTS YOU, RIFFRAF!

RIGHT. BRING HIM ROUND. COME HERE, ALL! MAKE HASTE!

SPLASH!

HASTING'S THE WORD...

SURELY IT'S NOT 1066 YET?

WHO... WHAT...? HELP!

BY TOUTATIS, THIS IS THE END OF ME! ALL THESE NORMANS... SO MANY OF THEM! THEY LOOK SO FIERCE... HELP! THEY'RE GOING TO KILL ME... THEIR CHIEF IS COMING TOWARDS ME...

GO ON, THEN! FRIGHTEN US!

23

* EAGER BEAVER. BUT DESPITE THE CASTOR ACTION FAVOURED BY OLEAGINUS, AMORICAN CAMPAIGNS SELDOM WENT ON OILED WHEELS.

28

MISSION ACCOMPLISHED, THE PATROL RETURNS TO CAMP...

WELL, SO WHAT'S GOING ON DOWN ON THE BEACH?

ON THE BEACH?

OH, NOTHING.

JUST A FEW BATHERS HAVING A LITTLE ARGUMENT...

IT'S ALL THIS THUNDER IN THE AIR...

AND YOU'LL BE GETTING A REPORT. IN TRIPLICATE...

MEANWHILE, IN THE TENT OF THE FEROCIOUS TIMANDAHAF...

HAVE YOU KIDNAPPED JUSTFORKIX?

YOUR EXPERT?

EXPERT?

?

YOUR EXPERT KNOWS IT ALL, AND WE SHALL LEAVE ONCE HE'S TAUGHT US ALL HE KNOWS.

OH YES, HE'S AN EXPERT ON LUTETIAN DANCING... BUT I CAN TEACH YOU ABOUT ROCK MYSELF...

THIS IS THE WAY... ZING! ZOOM! ZING! ZOOM!

THEN YOU GO LIKE THIS... ZOOM! ZING! ZOOM! ZING!

LOOK, IS YOUR FRIEND MAKING FUN OF ME, FOOLING ABOUT LIKE THAT?

STOP IT, OBELIX. THE NORMANS DIDN'T COME HERE TO LEARN DANCING.

WELL, HE NEEDN'T THINK I'M DANCING ATTENDANCE ON HIM! FOOLING ABOUT, INDEED... BARBARIAN!

TEEHEEHEE! YOU SOUNDED JUST LIKE CACOFONIX THE BARD!

OH, VERY CLEVER!

WOULD YOU TWO MIND PAYING ATTENTION TO ME FOR A MOMENT?!?

33

WHILE ASTERIX IS HELD HOSTAGE BY THE NORMANS...

OBELIX IS SURE TO COME BACK, TIMANDAHAF, NEVER FEAR!

WHAT DO YOU MEAN, NEVER FEAR??!!

FRESH CREAM

...OBELIX GOES TIRELESSLY ON IN PURSUIT OF CACOFONIX THE BARD...

NEVER MIND, DOGMATIX! I'LL TEACH YOU TO SNIFF OUT BARDS AND YOU'LL GROW INTO A BIG STRONG DOGGIE...

...PICKING THE ODD BOAR ALONG HIS WAY TO STILL THE PANGS OF HUNGER...

... WHAT A COUPLE WE SHALL MAKE, WITH MY BRAINS AND YOUR STRENGTH!

...AND CASUALLY ELIMINATING SUCH ROMAN PATROLS AS ARE MISGUIDED ENOUGH TO CROSS HIS PATH.

NO POINT IN STOPPING HIM... SOL LUCET OMNIBUS, AS WE SAY AT HOME. LET'S GO BACK AND CARVE A REPORT IN TRIPLICATE.

GETTING TO BE A REAL CHISELLER, AREN'T YOU?

WHOA THERE! CALM DOWN! STOP REARING! WHOA!

?

WE MET A MAN MAKING SUCH AWFUL NOISES MY OXEN STAMPEDED!

YOU SEE, WE MUST BE ON THE RIGHT TRACK, DOGMATIX! THIS IS THE WAY TO FOLLOW A BARD'S SCENT!

OH YES, I SAW A HORSEMAN GO BY, BUT THE WAY HE WAS SINGING HE CAN'T HAVE BEEN A BARD!

MOOOOO!

OH YES, HE CAME THIS WAY. THE MILK TURNED JUST THEN!

AND FURTHER ON...

CACOFONIX'S HORSE! WE'VE FOUND HIM! YOU SEE, DOGMATIX, THERE'S NO DIFFERENCE BETWEEN BARDS AND MENHIRS!

SELFSERVIX

CACOFONIX! IT'S US! YOOHOO!

CACO...???

ER... DO YOU HAPPEN TO HAVE SEEN A BARD, MR... ER...?

SELFSERVIX, AT YOUR SERVICE... OH YES, I'VE SEEN A BARD ALL RIGHT, BY TOUTATIS!

HE COULDN'T PAY FOR THE MEAL HE ATE, HE SUGGESTED SINGING FOR HIS SUPPER ONCE HE STARTED I TOLD HIM IT WAS ON THE HOUSE...

... AND MY CUSTOMERS EVEN OFFERED HIM ANOTHER MEAL TO SHUT UP... SO HE GOT ANNOYED... AND NOW THE HOUSE IS ON ME! ♪ ♫SOBS♫ ♪

HE LEFT ME HIS HORSE AS COMPENSATION...

WELL, IF CACOFONIX IS GOING TO PAY HIS WAY BY SINGING HE WON'T GET FAR!

THERE HE IS!

CACOFONIX! YOOHOO! WAIT FOR US!

HA! I KNEW IT! THEY CAN'T DO WITHOUT ME IN THE VILLAGE. TOO BAD! I'VE GOT MY CAREER TO THINK OF!

31

36

THINGS ARE GOING FROM BAD TO WORSE IN THE NORMAN CAMP...

THESE SAUSAGES IN CREAM SAUCE ARE VERY GOOD!

SHUT UP, BY THOR!

BANG!

YOU'RE HAVING ME ON! I WON'T WAIT ANY LONGER! THE HOSTAGES WILL BE EXECUTED! SOMEONE GO AND GET THE GAULISH EXPERT OFF THE LONGSHIP!

LONGSHIP?

ONE OF OUR VESSELS. WE CAN USE EITHER SAIL OR OARS.

I KNEW YOUR FAVOURITE SPORT WAS SCULLING!

PUT THIS ONE IN CHAINS AND TAKE THEM BOTH UP THE CLIFF!

SOON AFTERWARDS...

I DON'T KNOW WHAT'S KEEPING OBELIX, BUT YOU MIGHT WAIT A LITTLE LONGER...

NO, I MIGHT NOT! YOU TWO HAVE A TABLE BOOKED FOR THE NEXT SITTING AT ODIN'S BANQUET!

BUT FIRST, IN THE CAUSE OF SCIENCE, YOU'RE GOING TO FLY OFF THIS CLIFF!

WOULDN'T YOU RATHER I GROVELLED AT YOUR FEET?

CHEER UP, JUSTFORKIX! SHOW THESE NORMANS HOW BRAVELY A GAUL CAN DIE!

YOU WAIT, THEY HAVEN'T FINISHED THEIR FUN YET!

RIGHT, I WANT YOU TO FLY OVER THERE TO THE LEFT. AFTER THAT I WANT YOU TO...

DON'T WORRY ABOUT THE ROUTE. IT'S NON-STOP, DIRECT...

33

37

38

YOU'RE NOT BEING ANY HELP, ASTERIX! I WAS MAKING THOSE FACES TO FRIGHTEN THEM!

TEEHEEHEE!

WHEN I USED TO MAKE FACES LIKE THAT AT HOME MY LITTLE SISTER WAS VERY FRIGHTENED, AND...

YOU KNOW, LITTLE SISTERS USUALLY SCARE MORE EASILY THAN BIG BARBARIANS.

WELL, THAT'S ENOUGH JOKING. LET'S GET BACK TO BUSINESS. NOW FOR YOUR FLYING DEMONSTRATION!

FIRSTHAF! SECONDHAF! TAKE HIM OVER TO THE RUNWAY!

IS THIS ALL RIGHT?

OH, I'M SO FRIGHTENED!

HE'S IN FINE FORM FOR FLYING NOW ... CAN HE TAKE OFF?

CHATTER! CHATTER!

ALL SYSTEMS GO! I REPEAT, ALL SYSTEMS GO! I ....

JUST A MOMENT! GNGNGN!

TCHAC!

WE'RE NOT GIVING IN WITHOUT A FIGHT!

JUSTFORKIX... CHARGE!

35

TCHAC!

I DON'T WANT THE EXPERT DAMAGED. CONCENTRATE ON THE LITTLE ONE, BY THOR!

LET HIM GO! LET HIM GO, I TELL YOU! YOU JUST LET HIM GO!

POFF!

THAT LITTLE GAUL IS REALLY PRETTY GOOD!

?

UFF!

FUNNY, I DIDN'T KNOW THERE WAS AN ECHO UP HERE...

!

YOOHOO! IT'S US, ASTERIX!

NORMANS, FOR THE VERY FIRST TIME OUR BARD CACOFONIX IS ABOUT TO APPEAR BEFORE YOU IN A SOLO PERFORMANCE!

SOMETHING TELLS ME IT'S THE VERY LAST TIME TOO! HE'LL SOON BE FLYING SOLO!

HAHAHAHAHA

GO ON, CACOFONIX! SHOW THEM WHAT YOU CAN DO!

THE AUDIENCE NEEDS WARMING UP A BIT...

PTOiiiNG!
TOiiiNG!

I LOVE A LASSIE, A BONNIE GAULISH LASSIE, SHE'S AS FAIR AS THE BOARS ROUND THE DOLMEN...

GET WITH IT! I'M REAL GONE!

OOOOH!

HELP!

OUCH! OUCH!

OW! OW! OW!

38

AFTER THEIR FIRST FLIGHT, WHICH IS SHORT AND SHARP, THE NORMANS REJOIN THEIR SHIP...

...BUT ONCE THEY ARE BACK ON BOARD, THINGS SOMEHOW SEEM DIFFERENT...

GET UP INTO THE CROW'S NEST, TOOCLEVERBYHAF!

THE TROUBLE IS...

WELL?

I FEEL SO FRIGHTENED UP THERE ALL ON MY OWN.

GET UP THAT MAST!

YES, CHIEF!

TCHIC!

EEEK!

CHIEF!

DON'T SNEAK UP BEHIND ME LIKE THAT! IT FRIGHTENS ME. WHAT DO YOU WANT?

IT'S THE MEN, CHIEF... THEY WANT YOU TO STOP SHOUTING LIKE THAT. IT FRIGHTENS THEM.

I FEAR OUR VOYAGE HAS BEEN ONLY TOO SUCCESSFUL...

SCRATCH! SCRATCH!

NEVER MIND, WE CAN FLY NOW...

FLY DOWN HERE, TOOCLEVERBYHAF!

YES, CHIEF!

SPLATCH!

YOU... YOU DON'T THINK THEY WERE HAVING US ON, CHIEF?

MAYBE, MAYBE NOT... ANYWAY, WE MUST BE CAREFUL IN FUTURE!

43

BACK IN THE VILLAGE OUR FRIENDS GET A TRIUMPHANT RECEPTION...

COME ON, THEN! WHY DON'T THEY COME ON?

YES, O CHIEF VITALSTATISTIX, YOUR NEPHEW IS NOW A TRUE FEARLESS GAUL!

I KNEW I COULD COUNT ON YOU, ASTERIX!

SNIFF! SNIFF!

OBELIX TAKES JUSTFORKIX IN HAND...

I'LL TEACH YOU HOW TO HUNT... WE'LL START WITH RABBITS, GO ON TO ROMAN PATROLS, AND WORK OUR WAY UP TO WILD BOAR!

LIKE MANY OTHER STARS, THE BARD LIKES TO DESCRIBE HIS HITS...

THEY STAMPED, THEY JUMPED UP AND DOWN, THEY TRIED TO GET AT ME!

YOU SHOULD GO FAR... THE FARTHER THE BETTER.

O GETAFIX, DO YOU THINK THE NORMANS HAD THE RIGHT IDEA WHEN THEY WANTED TO KNOW THE MEANING OF FEAR?

OF COURSE, ASTERIX!

IT'S ONLY WHEN YOU KNOW FEAR THAT YOU BECOME TRULY BRAVE! COURAGE LIES IN OVERCOMING YOUR FEAR!

AND SURE ENOUGH, THE NORMANS HAVE FOUGHT THEIR FEAR AND OVERCOME IT. THEY ARE STILL BRAVE, AND THEIR TABLES ARE BOOKED IN VALHALLA!

I ONLY ASKED IF THEY'D MADE ANY GOOD CONQUESTS LATELY.

YOU MIGHT HAVE KNOWN THAT WAS A NORSE CHESTNUT!

AS FOR JUSTFORKIX, HIS HOLIDAY IN THE BRACING AIR OF ARMORICA IS OVER. THE TIME HAS COME FOR HIM TO GO HOME TO LUTETIA. THE VILLAGERS GIVE HIM A SPLENDID FAREWELL BANQUET, AND CACOFONIX IS INVITED, SINCE IT IS, AFTER ALL, THANKS TO THE BARD THAT ALL'S WELL THAT ENDS WELL...

OH YEAH!

UDERZO & GOSCINNY

THE END

PRINTED IN BELGIUM BY
proost
INTERNATIONAL BOOK PRODUCTION